dedicated to
DAD

First published in Great Britain in 1997
by Ragged Bears Limited,
Ragged Appleshaw,
Andover,
Hampshire SP11 9HX

Copyright © 1997 by Nila Aye

The right of Nila Aye to be identified as the illustrator of this work has been asserted.

A CIP record of this book is available from the British Library

ISBN 1 85714 119 9

Printed in Hong Kong

Nila's Little Blue Book of Nursery Rhymes

By NILA AYE

RAGGED BEARS

Betty Blue

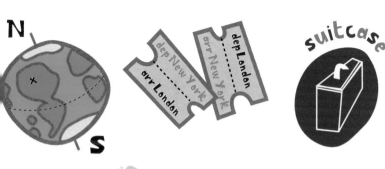

C<small>A</small>N <small>Y</small>O<small>U</small> F<small>I</small>N<small>D</small> H<small>E</small>R M<small>A</small>T<small>C</small>H<small>I</small>N<small>G</small> <small>SH</small>O<small>E</small>?

Little **Betty Blue**

Lost her holiday shoe.

What can little Betty do?

Give her another

To match the other,

And then she may walk out in two.

Bobby Shafto's

gone to sea,
Silver buckles on his knee;
He'll come back and marry me,
Bonny Bobby Shafto!

Bobby Shafto's bright and fair,
Combing down his yellow hair;
He's my love for evermore,
Bonny Bobby Shafto.

One, two, three, four, five,

Once I caught a fish alive.

Six, seven, eight, nine, ten,

Then I let it go again.

2 3 4

1 5

LEFT

7 8 9

10

Little finger

6

RIGHT

Why did you let it go?
Because it bit my finger so.
Which finger did it bite?
This little finger on the right.

the Meadow

Little Boy Blue

Come blow your horn,
The sheep's in the meadow,
The cow's in the corn.
But where is the boy
Who looks after the sheep?
He's under the haystack, fast asleep.

the Corn

the Haystack

the Horn

zzzzzz

BOY BLUE

Hey diddle di

The cat and the fiddle,
The cow jumped
   over the moon.
The little dog laughed
To see such sport,
And the dish ran away
   with the spoon.

Old Mother Hubbard

Went to the cupboard,
To fetch her poor dog a bone;
But when she got there,
The cupboard was bare
And so the poor dog had none.

CUPBOARD

BARE

She went to the baker's
To buy him some bread;
But when she came back
The poor dog was dead.

BREAD

COFFIN

She went to the undertaker's
To buy him a coffin;
But when she came back
The poor dog was laughing.

PIPE

She took a clean dish
To get him some tripe;
But when she came back
he was smoking a pipe.

CHAIR

BEER

She went to the ale-house
To buy him some beer;
But when she came back
The dog sat in a chair.

She went to the tavern
For white wine and red;
But when she came back
The dog stood on his head.

WINE

She went to the fruiterer's
To buy him some fruit;
But when she came back
He was playing the flute.

FLUTE

FRUIT

GOAT

She went to the tailor's
To buy him a coat;
But when she came back
He was riding a goat.

←- HAT

CAT

She went to the hatter's
To buy him a hat;
But when she came back
He was feeding the cat.

WIG

She went to the barber's
To buy him a wig;
But when she came back
He was dancing a jig.

NEWSPAPER

She went to the cobbler's
To buy him some shoes;
But when she came back
He was reading the news.

SHOES

She went to the seamstress
To buy him some linen;
But when she came back
The dog was a-spinning.

SPINNING WHEEL

She went to the hosier's
To buy him some hose;
But when she came back
He was dressed in his clothes.

CLOTHES

The dame made a curtsy,
The dog made a bow;
The dame said, "Your servant."
The dog said, "Bow-wow."

CURTSY   BOW

Dickery Dickery Dare

The pig flew up in the air.

The man in brown soon brought him down,

Dickery Dickery Dare

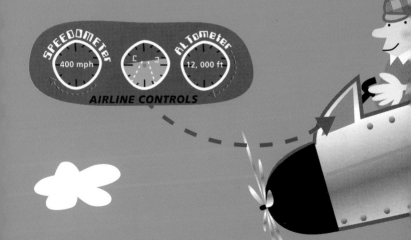

SPEEDOMETER

400 mph

ALTIMETER

12, 000 ft

AIRLINE CONTROLS

Little Jack Horner sat in a corner,
Eating a Christmas pie;
He put in his thumb,
And pulled out a **PLUM**,
And said, "What a good boy am I!"

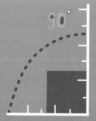

90°

a corner

the Baker

the Candlestick Maker

the Butcher

Rub-a-dub-dub,

Three men in a tub,
And who do you think they be?
The butcher, the baker, the candlestick maker;
Turn 'em out, knaves all three.

Wee Willie Winkie

runs through the town,
Upstairs and downstairs,
in his night-gown,

DOWNSTAIRS

Rapping at the windows,
  crying through the locks
Are the children in their beds,
  for it's past eight o'clock?